Trumpet Sonata
after Richard Strauss

Thomas Oehler & Jonathan Freeman-Attwood

Trumpet in B♭ or C & piano

Piano score

BOOSEY & HAWKES

Boosey & Hawkes Music Publishers Ltd
www.boosey.com

Published by Boosey & Hawkes Music Publishers Ltd
Aldwych House
71–91 Aldwych
London
WC2B 4HN

www.boosey.com

ISMN 979-0-060-13652-8
ISBN 978-1-78454-554-3

This impression 2020

Printed by Halstan:
Halstan UK, 2–10 Plantation Road, Amersham, Bucks, HP6 6HJ. United Kingdom
Halstan DE, Weißliliengasse 4, 55116 Mainz. Germany

Music origination by Raimonds Zelmenis

CONTENTS

Trumpet Sonata after Richard Strauss

Duration: 25 minutes

First recording:

Linn Records CKD 621, *Richard Strauss and the Viennese Trumpet*,
by Jonathan Freeman-Attwood (trumpet) and Chiyan Wong (piano)

PREFACE

A Richard Strauss Trumpet Sonata

If there was ever a composer in the modern era from whom instrumentalists would hanker for a sonata or concerto, Richard Strauss must be right up there. His wide-ranging orchestral and operatic creations bleed with gloriously idiomatic writing for every instrument, and yet only the piano, violin, clarinet (in tandem with the bassoon) oboe and horn can really claim to have bespoke solo works from Strauss's seamlessly productive workshop from the 1880s to the late 1940s, and collectively they form only a small proportion of the composer's output.

In a series of recordings from Linn, 're-imagining' solo repertoire from the previous four centuries for the relatively recent duo of the modern trumpet and piano has been the stimulus. Other programmes have followed various types of transcription but our 'Sonata after Richard Strauss' extends well beyond a redeployment of the composer's music to fit a new idiom. Here we have a journey of two musicians spending, on and off, nearly five years figuring out how to create a significant concert piece which Strauss might have envisaged – and one, we hope, which will fill the gaping chasm of 'serious' late-Romantic recital for trumpet players, to be performed *in toto* or as *drei Konzertstücke*. Orchestral trumpet players began to explore the chamber potential of their instruments only in the first half of the 20th century – though in Germany less than in France, where *pièces de concours* flourished in the solo-infused world of the Paris Conservatoire. Apart from Karl Pilss (1935) and Paul Hindemith (1939), few trumpet sonatas exist within the model of mainstream Austro-German traditions of the 19th century.

The means of creating this sonata have necessitated five broad categories of engagement: (i) composing new material, (ii) the significant reassignment of existing material, (iii) arranging *and* transforming material for a radical new context or purpose, (iv) reducing or adapting original material to fit the chamber idiom, and (v) making small changes to suit the instrumental idiom. In terms of creative collaboration, one person thought up the idea and selected the majority of original Strauss pieces (the trumpet player) and the other (the composer) took material from a series of practical workshops we undertook, and then crafted the material into a three-movement sonata.

Starting with a relatively empty canvas, the first questions to be addressed were simple: to plan a sonata form for the first movement, a broad lyrical *adagio* second movement in ABA form, and a classic rondo for the last movement. The challenge with the first movement was practical on two fronts. Most solo trumpet pieces last only around fifteen minutes because of the stamina required to play a brass instrument with few points of rest; compressing a sonata form in the opulent language of Strauss would present additional challenges. Second, there are few Strauss sonata form templates such as one could find with, say, Brahms. *Ein Heldenleben* is a sonata form but too grand in scale to be practically helpful (though 'Des Helden Widersacher' (The Hero's Adversaries) and the famous battle scene provided the germs for some agitated figuration in the development).

That left us with the Violin Sonata, op 18. Taking the signposts of its first movement as our guide, we accepted that ours would be longer than most trumpet sonata movements, though slightly shorter than the violin original. The opening theme of op 18 is heroic and instantly lyrical – as you might expect of Strauss in E flat major – but it failed to resonate with our understanding of Strauss's view of the trumpet. Instead, a dotted anacrusis would propel us into a figurative realm instantly referencing the orchestral provenance of Strauss's trumpet-writing. It would evolve with the slow ratcheting up of rhythmic and melodic tension, leading to a climax on the note that so often sits at Strauss's summit, a top C natural. The kind of epic and modulating kick-start we identified was partly inspired by the swagger of the song, 'In der Campagna', op 42, no 2.

The initial lyrical theme of our first movement is soon abandoned for a freshly composed link to a new idea (from the short quasi-recitativo song 'Die Verschwiegenen', op 10, no 6). This is heavily arranged and reconfigured from the original song, metricised and given a flowing piano accompaniment before turning to the bold homophonic exhortation that appears at the equivalent point in the Violin Sonata. All these sections are given a structural length which serves the abstract 're-invention' of a sonata within the technical possibilities of the trumpet.

The development, and the link before it, is either newly composed or submitted to both light and heavy alteration. Seasoned Straussians will enjoy spotting the occasional references to other works – deliberate or serendipitous – and if there is ever uncertainty over which material is *echt* Strauss, partly Strauss or *pasticcio* Strauss, the authors will feel a degree of gentle satisfaction! The recapitulation follows the usual form, with one particularly extended section taken from the original sonata compressed for the sake of balance and economy. There is, for instance, no reflective return to the first lyrical subject of the Violin Sonata, but a new and bold coda which catapults the theme into the highly articulated patterning of Strauss's most exercised horn-writing.

The second movement is essentially a reduction of the rich string theme which appears after the sunrise at the opening of *Also sprach Zarathustra* – and, specifically, 'Von den Hinterweltlern' ('Of those in the background world'), with the piano introduction fashioned from its final phrase. The middle section is intended to provide an animated contrast, a tussle or battle of wills, where the heroic song 'Liebeshymnus' (the third of five songs in Strauss's short op 32 cycle) is offset against original material to extend its dramatic impact, before a return to the *Also sprach* theme and a hybrid coda of original and invented Strauss.

The third movement rondo employs a freshly composed theme with a passing regard for the equivalent place in the Second Horn Concerto. The final movement of the Sonatina no 1 in F for wind instruments, 'From an invalid's workshop', contains a glorious oboe tune which is shamelessly purloined and accompanied with a similarly mischievous running commentary of quavers from the main rondo theme. Attempting to retain fluency and quixotic melodic variety and character, we turned to *Ariadne auf Naxos* and Zerbinetta's famously flirtatious aria where she suggests to the newly-chaste Ariadne that she find another man, whilst claiming (in the same breath) that she's a one-man woman whilst 'every man was like a God'. Such quixotic moods suited the episodes of our rondo.

In the course of these endeavours, I am grateful above all to Thomas Oehler. His central role as an exquisite craftsman is second only to Strauss himself, and he has been an incessantly inspiring collaborator throughout. Our article describing the motivations and creation of the work appears in www.boosey.com/SonataAfterStrauss.

Thanks are offered to the Royal Academy of Music, and specifically to my remarkable colleagues there. Professor Timothy Jones and Chiyan Wong, and internationally renowned trumpet players Mark David, Reinhold Friedrich and Jeroen Berwaerts have all played an invaluable part. That Linn Records agreed that I should record the Sonata (released in March 2020), as the centre-piece of a Viennese project, is down to the forbearance of Philip Hobbs.

Finally, thanks are given to the late James Watson – one of the greatest British trumpeters ever and a teacher extraordinaire – who, when I mooted the idea of creating a 'Strauss' Trumpet Sonata in 2010, told me that it was reckless, to forget it and to practise harder instead (whilst secretly hoping it might happen). Whether he was right, wrong or both, we dedicate this work to his memory.

Jonathan Freeman-Attwood
July 2019

VORWORT

Eine Trompetensonate nach Richard Strauss

Unter den KomponistInnen der modernen Geschichte, von denen sich InstrumentalistInnen eine Sonate oder ein Konzert ersehnten, gehörte Richard Strauss doch sich zu den Beliebtesten. Seine umfangreichen Orchester- und Opernschöpfungen strotzen geradezu vor herrlich instrumentengerechten Stimmen. Doch aus der von den 1880er bis zu den späten 1940er Jahren unablässig produktiven Werkstatt von Strauss können nur das Klavier, die Violine, die Klarinette (zusammen mit dem Fagott), die Oboe und das Horn auf speziell für sie geschaffene Solostücke verweisen. Zusammen bilden diese Solostücke nur einen kleinen Teil von Strauss' Œuvre.

In einer Reihe von Aufnahmen bei Linn Records „empfand" man Solorepertoire aus den vergangenen vier Jahrhunderten für die relativ neue Duokombination aus moderner Trompete und Klavier „nach". Darauf folgten diverse Transkriptionen, aber unsere „Sonate nach Richard Strauss" geht weit über die Anpassung von Strauss' Musik für eine neue Besetzung hinaus. Die hier vorliegende Sonate spiegelt eine Reise zweier Musiker wider, die fast fünf Jahre lang – mit Unterbrechungen – versuchten, ein gewichtiges Konzertstück zu schaffen, wie Strauss es sich vorgestellt haben mag. Wir hoffen auch, dass dieses Konzertstück den Mangel an „ernsten" spätromantischen Vortragswerken für Trompeter überbrückt. Die Sonate soll entweder *in toto* oder als *drei Konzertstücke* vorgetragen werden. Erst in der ersten Hälfte des 20. Jahrhunderts begannen Orchestertrompeter das kammermusikalische Potential ihrer Instrumente zu erkunden – weniger in Deutschland als in Frankreich, wo in der solistisch ausgerichteten Welt des Pariser Konservatoriums zahlreiche *Pièces de concours* florierten. Im Rahmen der gängigen österreichisch-deutschen Tradition des 19. Jahrhunderts gibt es jedoch außer den Trompetensonaten von Karl Pilß (1935) und Paul Hindemith (1939) nur wenige solche Werke.

Um die hier vorliegende Sonate zu schaffen, waren grob umrissen fünf Arbeitsgänge erforderlich: (1) Komposition von neuem Material, (2) eine erhebliche Neuzuordnung bestehenden Materials, (3) Bearbeitung *und* Transformation von Material für einen völlig neuen Kontext und Zweck, (4) Begrenzung und Anpassung originalen Materials an die kammermusikalischen Eigenheiten und (5) kleine Änderungen zur Anpassung an die Besonderheiten des Instruments. Unser kreativer Prozess verlief wie folgt: Der Trompeter stellte eine Idee vor und wählte den Großteil der Werke von Strauss aus. Der Komponist nutzte Material aus einer Reihe von uns veranstalteter Workshops und formte es dann zu einer dreisätzigen Sonate.

Ausgehend von einem relativ leeren Blatt waren die ersten Entscheidungen einfach: Konzipiere eine Sonatenstruktur für den ersten Satz, ein ausladendes lyrisches *Adagio* in ABA-Form für den zweiten Satz und ein klassisches Rondo für den letzten Satz. Die Herausforderung beim ersten Satz bestand in praktischen Erwägungen in zweierlei Hinsicht: Die meisten Solostücke für Trompete dauern nur ca. 15 Minuten aufgrund der erforderlichen physischen Kondition beim Spielen eines Blechblasinstruments ohne größere Pausen. Das Komprimieren von Strauss' opulenter Tonsprache in eine spielbare Sonatenform erwies sich als besonders schwierig. Zweitens gibt es im Vergleich mit zum Beispiel Brahms nur wenige Sonatenform-Vorbilder bei Strauss. *Ein Heldenleben* ist ein Sonatensatz, aber zu grandios, um tatsächlich behilflich zu sein (auch wenn „Des Helden Widersacher" und die berühmte Kampfszene Keime für einige aufgeregte Verzierungen in der Durchführung lieferten).

Da blieb uns nur die Violinsonate op. 18 übrig. Der erste Satz lieferte uns die Eckpfeile als Orientierungshilfen. Dabei akzeptierten wir, dass der Satz länger als die meisten Trompetensonatensätze wird. Wir bemühten uns jedoch, unseren ersten Satz im Vergleich mit dem Satz in der Violinsonate etwas kürzer zu halten. Das einleitende Thema von op. 18 ist heroisch und sofort lyrisch – wie man das von einem Strauss in Es-Dur erwartet. Aber dieser Anfang entsprach nicht unseren Vorstellungen, wie Strauss für die Trompete geschrieben hätte. Stattdessen katapultiert uns ein punktierter Auftakt in ein figuratives Reich, das sofort an die Trompetenstimmen aus Strauss' Orchesterwerken erinnert. In diesem sich entwickelnden Reich wird die Schraube der rhythmischen und melodischen Spannungen langsamen angeschraubt und führt zu einem Höhepunkt auf der Note, die so häufig Strauss' Gipfel schmückt, das hohe C. Der von uns entworfene epische und modulierende Kickstart wurde zum Teil von dem großtuerischen Gehabe in dem Lied „In der Campagna“ op. 42, Nr. 2 angeregt.

Darauf folgt das lyrische Thema des ersten Satzes aus der Violinsonate. Allerdings räumt es bald einem neukomponierten Übergang zu einem neuen Gedanken (aus dem kurzen rezitativähnlichen Lied „Die Verschwiegenen“ op. 10, Nr. 6) das Feld. Dieser „Den Verschwiegenen“ entlehnte musikalische Gedanke wurde stark bearbeitet und umgestellt, in eine Taktart gefasst und mit einer fließenden Klavierbegleitung versehen. Darauf folgt die gleiche forsche homophone Ermahnung, die an der entsprechenden Stelle in der Violinsonate erscheint. Alle diese Abschnitte erhalten die strukturelle Länge, die zu der abstrakten „Neuerfindung“ einer Sonate im Rahmen der Möglichkeiten der Trompete passt.

In der Durchführung und im Übergang davor findet man entweder neukomponiertes Material oder leichte bzw. starke Bearbeitungen bestehenden Materials. Kenner von Strauss werden ihren Spaß beim Entziffern gelegentlicher Referenzen – absichtlich oder zufällig – zu anderen Werken des Komponisten haben. Sollte es jemals Unsicherheiten geben, welches Material ausschließlich echter Strauss, teilweise echter Strauss oder im Stile von Strauss ist, würden wir uns nur geehrt fühlen. Die Reprise folgt der gewöhnlichen Formvorlage und übernimmt einen besonders langen Abschnitt aus der Violinsonate, der hier zum Zwecke der Ausgewogenheit und Ökonomie komprimiert wurde. In unserer Sonate gibt es zum Beispiel keine reflektierende Rückkehr zum ersten lyrischen Thema, sondern eine neue und forsche Koda, die das Thema in ein äußerst artikuliertes Modellieren von Strauss' am meisten verwendeten Horneinsätzen katapultiert.

Der zweite Satz beruht im Wesentlichen auf einer reduzierten Fassung des satten Streicherthemas, das nach dem Sonnenaufgang zu Beginn von *Also sprach Zarathustra* und besonders in „Von den Hinterweltlern“ auftaucht, wobei die letzte Phrase des Streicherthemas Ausgangspunkt für die Klaviereinleitung hier war. Der Mittelabschnitt des zweiten Satzes ist als ein lebhafter Kontrast – ein Gerangel oder geistiger Wettstreit – gedacht, wo das heroische Lied „Liebeshymnus“ (das dritte der fünf Lieder in Strauss' kurzem Zyklus op. 22) aus anderem originalen Material hervorgehoben wird, um die dramatische Wirkung zu verlängern. Dann kehrt das *Also-sprach-Zarathustra*-Thema wieder zurück und mündet in eine hybride Koda aus originalem und erfundenem Strauss.

Das Rondo des dritten Satzes zieht ein frisch komponiertes Thema heran mit einem flüchtigen Verweis auf die entsprechende Stelle im zweiten Hornkonzert. Der letzte Satz der Sonatina Nr. 1 in F-Dur, „Aus der Werkstatt eines Invaliden“, enthält eine herrliche Oboenmelodie, die hier schamlos ausgenutzt und mit einem ähnlich frechen laufenden Achtelnotenkommentar aus dem Hauptthema des Rondos begleitet wird. In dem Versuch, den fließenden und quirligen melodischen Reichtum und Charakter zu erhalten, wandten wir uns zu *Ariadne auf Naxos* und Zerbinettas berühmt flirtender Arie. Dort versucht Zerbinetta, die verlassene Ariadne zu trösten, indem sie Ariadne Hoffnung zuspricht, einen neuen Mann zu finden. Im selben Atemzug behauptet Zerbinetta, die eigentlich jeden Mann vergöttert, sie wäre eine Ein-Mann-Frau. Solche quirligen Stimmungswechsel passten für die Episoden unseres Rondos.

Für die Arbeit an dieser Sonate bin ich besonders Thomas Oehler sehr dankbar. Er spielte eine zentrale Rolle, und seine handwerklichen Fähigkeiten werden höchstens von Strauss selbst überboten. Es war die ganze Zeit äußerst anregend, mit ihm zusammenzuarbeiten. Unser Artikel, der die Gedankengänge und den Schaffungsprozess beschreibt, erscheint in www.boosey.com/SonataAfterStrauss.

Herzlichen Dank an die Royal Academy of Music, London und besonders an meine hervorragenden Kollegen dort. Professor Timothy Jones und Chiyan Wong sowie die international bekannten Trompeter Mark David, Reinhold Friedrich und Jeroen Berwaerts haben alle einen unschätzbaren Beitrag geleistet. Linn Records Zustimmung zu meiner Einspielung der Sonate als Herzstück eines Wiener Projekts (Veröffentlichung im März 2020) ist der Geduld von Philip Hobbs zu verdanken.

Schließlich möchte ich mich bei dem nunmehr verstorbenen James Watson bedanken – einem großartigen britischen Trompeter und ausgezeichneten Lehrer. Als ich ihm 2010 andeutete, ich würde eine Trompetensonate im Stile von Strauss schaffen, sagte er zu mir, das wäre waghalsig, ich sollte es sein lassen und stattdessen mehr üben (während er doch heimlich hoffte, es würde geschehen). Ungeachtet, ob er nun recht hatte oder nicht, oder beides, haben wir das Werk seinem Andenken gewidmet.

Jonathan Freeman-Attwood
Juli 2019

(Übersetzung: Elke Hockings)

PRÉFACE

Une Sonate pour trompette d'après Richard Strauss

S'il existe un compositeur de l'époque moderne dont les instrumentistes rêveraient de pouvoir jouer une sonate ou un concerto, ce serait assurément Richard Strauss. Ses créations orchestrales et lyriques dans tous les genres regorgent d'écriture magnifiquement accordée à chaque instrument et, pourtant, seuls le piano, le violon, la clarinette (en tandem avec le basson), le hautbois et le cor peuvent se prévaloir d'œuvres solistes spécifiques issues de l'activité compositionnelle de Strauss, des années 1880 à la fin des années 1940, qui ne forment qu'une faible proportion de la production du compositeur.

L'impulsion donnée à ce projet provint d'une série d'enregistrements réalisés sous le label Linn Records « re-imaginant » un répertoire soliste destiné à la formation en duo relativement récente de la trompette moderne et du piano et recouvrant les quatre derniers siècles. D'autres démarches se sont attachées à divers types de transcriptions mais notre « Sonate d'après Richard Strauss » s'étend au-delà du redéploiement de la musique du compositeur adapté au langage instrumental. Il s'agit ici du travail effectué pendant presque cinq années par deux musiciens en vue de créer une pièce de concert caractéristique, telle qu'aurait pu la concevoir Strauss, qui puisse être interprétée intégralement ou divisée en trois *Konzertstücke* – et qui, espérons-le, comblera le grand vide existant dans le répertoire de récital romantique tardif de la trompette. Les trompettistes d'orchestre ne commencèrent à explorer le potentiel chambriste de leur instrument que dans la première moitié du XXème siècle – moins en Allemagne qu'en France où les « pièces de concours » prospérèrent grâce à la tradition soliste du Conservatoire de Paris. A part celles de Karl Pilss (1935) et de Paul Hindemith (1939), il n'existe que peu de sonates pour trompette rattachées au modèle austro-germanique du XIXème siècle.

La création de cette sonate impliqua cinq larges angles d'approche : (i) la composition de matériel original, (ii) la redirection pertinente de matériel existant, (iii) l'arrangement *et* la transformation du matériel dans un contexte ou un objectif radicalement nouveaux, (iv) la réduction ou l'adaptation du matériel original au format de chambre et (v) les légères modifications nécessaires au jeu instrumental, et suscita la collaboration créatrice du trompettiste, initiateur de l'idée, qui sélectionna la plupart des pièces originales de Strauss et du compositeur qui compila le matériel élaboré au cours de séances pratiquées à deux et l'inséra dans une sonate en trois mouvements.

Partant d'un cadre relativement vierge, les réponses à apporter se présentaient, de prime abord, de façon simple : construire une forme sonate pour le premier mouvement, un large *adagio* lyrique de forme ABA pour le deuxième mouvement et un *rondo* classique pour le dernier mouvement. Le défi pratique à relever pour le premier mouvement était toutefois double. Tout d'abord, les pièces pour trompette soliste ne durent en général qu'environ quinze minutes du fait de la condition physique requise par l'interprétation d'une partie de cuivre sans temps de repos fréquents. Concentrer une forme sonate fidèle au style opulent de Strauss dans ces limites présentait une contrainte supplémentaire. Par ailleurs, on ne trouve que peu de « modèles » de forme sonate chez Strauss, tels qu'on en rencontre, par exemple, chez Brahms. Les dimensions du mouvement de sonate *Ein Heldenleben* s'avérèrent trop étendues pour servir pratiquement notre propos (bien que « Des Helden Widersacher » (« Les ennemis du héros ») et la célèbre scène de la bataille aient inspiré certaines configurations agitées du développement).

Il nous restait donc la Sonate pour violon, op.18. Guidés par la structure de son premier mouvement, nous décidâmes que le mouvement initial serait à la fois plus long que la plupart des mouvements de sonates pour trompette et légèrement plus court que celui de la sonate pour violon originale. Le thème initial de l'op.18, héroïque et immédiatement lyrique – ainsi qu'on peut l'attendre de Strauss en *mi* bémol majeur – ne correspondait pas à notre idée de la vision de Strauss sur la trompette. Une anacrouse pointée donnerait une meilleure impulsion vers un univers figuratif en référence immédiate à la source orchestrale de l'écriture pour trompette de Strauss, évoluant dans un lent engrenage de tensions rythmique et mélodique vers le sommet du *do* naturel aigu si fréquent chez Strauss. L'attaque épique et modulante que nous avons élaborée s'inspire en partie de l'éclat du Lied « *In der Campagna* », op.42, n°2.

Le thème lyrique principal de notre premier mouvement fait bientôt place à une transition inventée vers une nouvelle idée musicale (extraite du Lied court et presque récitatif « *Die Verschwiegenen* », op.10, n°6), largement remaniée et reconfigurée, mesurée et accompagnée d'une partie de piano fluide avant de prendre la forme impétueuse de l'exhortation homophone qui apparaît à l'endroit équivalent de la Sonate pour violon. Toutes ces sections sont d'une durée conforme à la « ré-invention » abstraite d'une sonate dans la limite des possibilités techniques de la trompette.

Le développement et la transition qui le précède sont soit nouvellement composées, soit plus ou moins fortement modifiées. Les Straussiens experts reconnaîtront avec plaisir telle ou telle référence à d'autres œuvres – voulue ou inattendue – et leur éventuelle incertitude sur l'appartenance du matériel musical à du Strauss *pur*, du Strauss partiel ou du Strauss pastiché remplira les auteurs d'un certain degré de délicieuse satisfaction ! La réexposition suit la forme traditionnelle, l'une des sections particulièrement étendue de la sonate originale y étant resserrée pour des raisons d'équilibre et d'économie. Il n'y a pas, par exemple, de reprise en reflet du premier thème lyrique de la Sonate pour violon mais une nouvelle et éclatante coda qui propulse le thème dans des configurations extrêmement articulées de la plus belle écriture de Strauss pour le cor.

Le deuxième mouvement se présente pour l'essentiel comme une réduction du riche thème des cordes qui apparaît après l'épisode de l'aube dans *Also sprach Zarathustra*, et, plus spécifiquement, de « *Von den Hinterweltlern* » (« venu des mondes lointains») dont la dernière phrase façonne l'introduction de piano. La section médiane est conçue en contraste animé, mêlée ou lutte des volontés, dans lequel le chant héroïque «*Liebeshymnus*» (troisième des cinq Lieder du cycle op.32 de Strauss) se détache du matériel original pour en augmenter la portée dramatique avant la reprise du thème de *Also sprach* et une coda imbriquant du matériel original de Strauss et du matériel inventé.

Le troisième mouvement en *rondo* présente un thème composé émaillé d'allusions au troisième mouvement du Deuxième concerto pour cor. Le mouvement final de la Sonatine n°1 pour instruments à vent, «Dans l'atelier d'un infirme», renferme une lumineuse mélodie de hautbois, empruntée sans vergogne et accompagnée d'un commentaire de croches tout aussi espiègles extraites du thème principal du *rondo*. De manière à maintenir une fluidité ainsi qu'un caractère et une diversité mélodique «romanesques», nous nous sommes tournés vers le fameux air suggestif de Zerbinetta de l'opéra *Ariadne auf Naxos* dans lequel elle suggère à la chaste Ariane de trouver un autre homme, tout en affirmant (dans le même souffle) être elle-même la femme d'un seul homme et que «chaque homme est un dieu». Cette ambiance «à la Don Quichotte» convenait parfaitement aux épisodes de notre *rondo*.

Ma gratitude s'adresse tout particulièrement à Thomas Oehler, à son rôle prépondérant d'artiste subtil ne le cédant qu'à Strauss lui-même et à sa collaboration sans cesse inspirée au cours de cette entreprise. Notre description des étapes de motivations et de création de l'œuvre figure sur le site www.boosey.com/SonataAfterStrauss.

Je remercie la Royal Academy of Music et, plus spécifiquement, mes collègues. Les professeurs Timothy Jones et Chiyan Wong, ainsi que les trompettistes de renommée internationale Mark David, Reinhold Friedrich et Jeroen Berwaerts ont tous joué un rôle précieux. L'accord donné par la société Linn Records à mon enregistrement de la Sonate comme pièce centrale d'un projet viennois (parution prévue en mars 2020) est dû à la ténacité de Philip Hobbs.

Enfin, je tiens à remercier, à titre posthume, James Watson – l'un des plus grands trompettistes britanniques de tous les temps et extraordinaire pédagogue – qui, alors que j'évoquai l'idée de créer une Sonate pour trompette d'après Strauss en 2010, me déclara que ce projet était irréfléchi, me conseilla de l'oublier (tout en secrètement espérant qu'il pourrait voir le jour) et de plutôt travailler plus dur mon instrument. Qu'il ait eu tort ou raison, nous dédions cette œuvre à sa mémoire.

Jonathan Freeman-Attwood
Juillet 2019

(Traduction Agnès Ausseur)

TRUMPET SONATA
after Richard Strauss

THOMAS OEHLER
& JONATHAN FREEMAN-ATTWOOD

I

A
mf
f
p

mf
mp
cresc
mf
mp
cresc
(cresc)
f
(cresc)
f
rit
B Un poco meno mosso ♩ = 110
mf
mf
p

34
mp
8
pp
37
cresc
(8)
cresc
mf
f
40
43
f

rit
46
dim
C a tempo ♩ = 110
49
p
mp dolce
p
52
54
mf
mp

56
mp
58
60
mf
63
mp

D
Più mosso ♩ = 120
p
f
mf
E
mp
fp
ff marcato
pp
ff

78
fpp
ff
fp
pp
82
p
ff
85
F
88
mp
mf
f

rit
92
p
f
G
a tempo
95
mf
f
98
mp
mp cresc
101
(cresc)
f
8
f

H
104
mp
f
mp
f
p sub
mp
107
mp
mf
mf
110
mp
I
Poco maestoso
113
Con moto
mf
mp

117
optional mute
f
f
120
mf
f
mp
123
mf
126
rit

J
Meno mosso ♩ = 100
130
open dolce
p
132
134
mf
mp
136

138
più mosso
poco accel
141
(accel)
144
a tempo subito
p sub
147
rit
K
a tempo
p

150
pp
153
mf
p
pp
156
ppp
L Più mosso ♩ = 120
160
f

163
166
ff
8
ff
3
3
3
169
espr
3
3
8
3
172
3

175
(ff)
f
178
f
cresc
181
cresc
(cresc)
ff
184
M
(cresc)
f
dim
ff
dim

poco rit
187
(dim)
(dim)
(poco rit)
191
(dim)
pp
(dim)
pp
Meno mosso ♩ = c112
194
pp
199
cresc
cresc

203
poco accel
(cresc)
(cresc)
206
(accel)
(cresc)
(cresc)
ff
N
209
Più mosso ♩ = 128
rit
ff
f
O
212
Tempo primo ♩ = 120
f

P
rit
dim

Un poco meno mosso ♩ = c102
241
mp dolce
p
243
245
mf
mp
247
mp

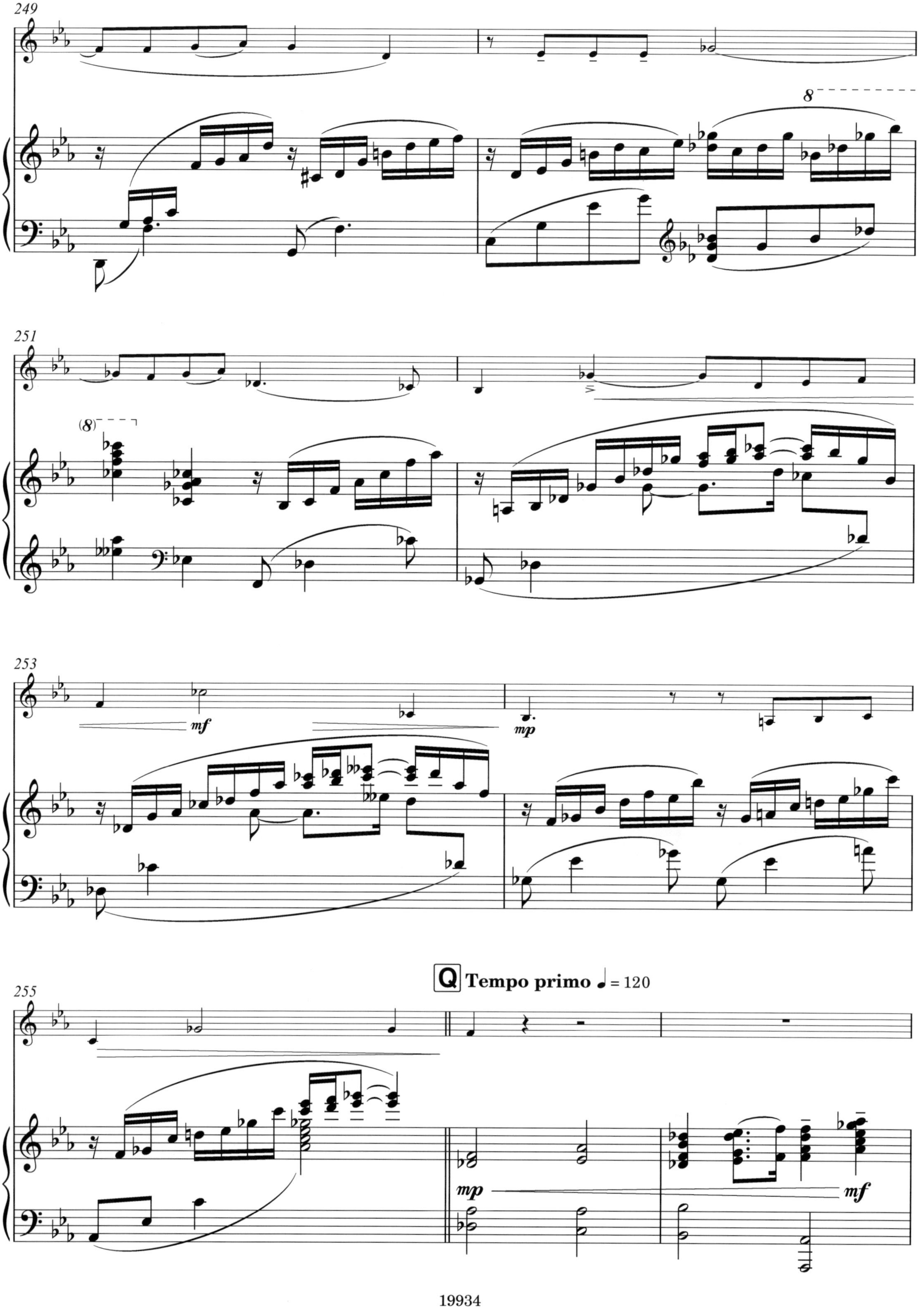
249
8
251
(8)
253
mf
mp
255
Q Tempo primo ♩ = 120
mp
mf

meno mosso
accel
a tempo
pp sub
p
f

267
ff marc
fp
pp
ff
270
273
R
f
276
p

S
280
p
f
283
mf
286
cresc
289
(cresc)
ff

espr

301
ff
ff
304
rit
T Vivo
6
8
7
3
5
6
f
3
307
3
3
3
3
3
3
3
310
f
3
3
3
3
3
3
f
3

313
fp
f
316
più mosso
mf
mf
319
rit
a tempo
f
f
322

II

Andante cantabile ♪ = 88
Trumpet in C
Piano
p
mf
5
p
10
mf
p
15
rit
A a tempo
mp espr
mp

cresc
(cresc)
cresc
(cresc)

B
38
f
f
42
C
ff
ff
46
p
mp
mf
51
mp

56
sfz
sfz
pp
mp
D
61
p
mf
66
accel
E
70
♪ = 106
mf
mf

73
76
F
f
mp
6
79
mf
3
82

85
3
f
f
6
3
6
88
6
6
mp
91
mf
cresc
cresc
G
94
f
f
6
6
6
6
6
6

rit

Tempo primo
rit
111
mp espr
p
ms
md
H
Andante cantabile ♪ = 100
115
mp
mf
121
mf
p
cresc
cresc
126
(cresc)
(cresc)
mf
mf
mp
mp

131
cresc
f
I
135
mf
cresc
139
cresc
ff
J
143
6
3

146
mp
mp
151
155
sfz
sfz
p
K
160
con sord
p
pp
p

III

17
mf
21
A
mf
25
29

B
33
mp
mp
37
41
46

50
54
poco rit
58
mf
Un poco meno mosso
62
C
Tempo primo
mp
mf

67
72
rit
a tempo
subito
mf
D
76
80

84
88
2:3
f
92
mf
96
mf

100
104
108
E
113
118
2:3
mp
p

F
122
mp
125
128
mf
mf
G
131

H
rit
a tempo
134
mp
mp
3
137
3
3
3
140
3
p
p
144
3
3
cresc
3
cresc
3

I
(cresc)
f
p sub
(cresc)
f
p sub
poco accel
cresc
cresc
f
f
(accel)
poco rit
a tempo
mp
mf
mf

J
165
p
mp
168
mp dolce
mp dolce
171
mf
mp
174
pp

K
= ♩. Un poco più mosso
177
cresc
pp
cresc
180
(cresc)
(cresc)
183
(cresc)
(cresc)
L
Tempo primo
186
f
f

191
195
199
2:3
f
203

M
207
f
211
215
N
218

222
226
230
234
poco rit
a tempo

238
242
poco rit
mf
Un poco meno mosso
mf
245
O
a tempo
249
mf

255
mf
260
265
270
f
(mf)

P
274
279
283
287
f
2:3
mf

291
Q
295
mf
299
303
307

311
mp
f
2:3
mf
f
315
320
R
324
f
f
2:3

328
2:3
332
337
S
342
p sub

346
2:3
mp
f
351
f
2:3
356
2:3
T
360
ff
2:3
ff
2:3
2:3

Trumpet Sonata

after Richard Strauss

Thomas Oehler & Jonathan Freeman-Attwood

Trumpet in B♭ or C & piano

Trumpet in C

BOOSEY & HAWKES

Boosey & Hawkes Music Publishers Ltd
www.boosey.com

TRUMPET SONATA
after Richard Strauss

Trumpet in C

THOMAS OEHLER
& JONATHAN FREEMAN-ATTWOOD

I

21
mf
mp
cresc
3
25
(cresc)
f
3
rit
B Un poco meno mosso ♩ = 110
29
Pno
mf
33
mp
37
cresc
mf
40
3
43
3
f
3
Pno

rit
C
a tempo ♩ = 110
mp dolce
mf
mp
D
Più mosso ♩ = 120
p
f
E
fp
Pno

F
rit
G a tempo
cresc
(cresc)
H
I Poco maestoso
Con moto
optional mute

124
Pno
127
rit
J
Meno mosso ♩ = 100
130
open dolce
134
mf
mp
138
più mosso
poco accel
142
(accel)
a tempo subito
146
rit
K
a tempo
150
154
mf
p
Più mosso ♩ = 120
L
Pno
158

cresc
(cresc)
M
dim
(dim)
poco rit
(poco rit)

Meno mosso ♩ = c112
pp
cresc
(cresc)
poco accel
(accel)
(cresc)
ff
N Più mosso ♩ = 128
rit
f
O Tempo primo ♩ = 120
mp
mf
f

226
229
232
236
P
Pno
rit
241
Un poco meno mosso ♩ = c102
mp dolce
245
249
252
256
Q
Tempo primo ♩ = 120
Pno
meno mosso
accel
VS

a tempo
R
2
Pno
S
cresc
(cresc)

295
298
302
ff
rit
T Vivo
306
Pno
309
f
312
fp
f
315
mf
più mosso
318
rit
a tempo
f
321

II

Andante cantabile ♪ = 88
Pno
rit
A
a tempo
mp espr
mf
p
cresc
1
mp
cresc
f
B
mf
f
ff
C
p
mp

sfz
sfz
D
accel
Pno
E
♪ = 106
mf
F
Pno
f
mf
f
Pno
G
mf
cresc
f
mp
rit
mf
mp
f

Tempo primo
rit
Pno
mp espr
H
Andante cantabile ♪ = 100
mf
mf
p
cresc
mf
1
mp
cresc
f
I
Pno
f
J
ff
mp
sfz
sfz
1
Pno
K
con sord
p

III

29
B
33
mp
39
45
52
58
poco rit
mf
Un poco meno mosso
C
64
Tempo primo
Pno
mp
70
rit
a tempo
subito
mf

D
f
mf
mf
E
Pno
VS

121
F
2:3
mp
125
129
G
mf
134
rit
H
a tempo
mp
139
p
143
cresc
147
I
poco accel
(cresc)
f
p sub
cresc
152
(accel)
poco rit
a tempo
(cresc)
f
Pno
156
161

J
p
mp
mp dolce
mf
mp
pp
K
Un poco più mosso
cresc
(cresc)
(cresc)
L
Tempo primo
f
f
2:3

206
Pno
M
f
210
Pno
214
218
N
224
230
poco rit
235
a tempo
241
poco rit
Un poco meno mosso
mf
246
O a tempo
Pno
252

257
mf
262
268
(mf)
P
274
279
284
2:3
f
289
mf
1
Q
295
1
mf
301
Pno
305

309
mp
f
2:3
315
320
R
f
325
2:3
f
331
ff
337
S
1
343
f
347
mp
f
352
358
T
ff

Published by Boosey & Hawkes Music Publishers Ltd
Aldwych House
71–91 Aldwych
London
WC2B 4HN

www.boosey.com

ISMN 979-0-060-13652-8
ISBN 978-1-78454-554-3

This impression 2020

Printed by Halstan:
Halstan UK, 2–10 Plantation Road, Amersham, Bucks, HP6 6HJ. United Kingdom
Halstan DE, Weißliliengasse 4, 55116 Mainz. Germany

Music origination by Raimonds Zelmenis

Trumpet Sonata
after Richard Strauss

Thomas Oehler & Jonathan Freeman-Attwood

Trumpet in B♭ or C & piano

Trumpet in B♭

BOOSEY & HAWKES

Boosey & Hawkes Music Publishers Ltd
www.boosey.com

TRUMPET SONATA

after Richard Strauss

Trumpet in B♭

THOMAS OEHLER
& JONATHAN FREEMAN-ATTWOOD

I

Allegro energico ♩ = 128

21
mf
mp
cresc
25
(cresc)
f
rit
B Un poco meno mosso ♩ = 110
29
Pno
mf
33
mp
37
cresc
mf
40
43
f
Pno

rit
C a tempo ♩ = 110
mp dolce
mf
mp
mp
mf
mp
D Più mosso ♩ = 120
1
p
f
mf
E
mp
fp
2
fp
p
3
Pno

F
rit
G a tempo
mp cresc
(cresc)
H
I Poco maestoso
Con moto
optional mute

Pno
rit
J
Meno mosso ♩ = 100
open dolce
mf
mp
più mosso
poco accel
(accel)
a tempo subito
rit
K
a tempo
mf
p
Più mosso ♩ = 120
L
Pno

162
165
8
ff
168
171
175
(ff)
3
179
f
3
cresc
182
(cresc)
M
185
f
dim
188
poco rit
(dim)
191
(poco rit)
(dim)
pp

194
Meno mosso ♩ = c112
pp
200
cresc
203
poco accel
(cresc)
206
(accel)
(cresc)
ff
N
209
Più mosso ♩ = 128
rit
f
O
Tempo primo ♩ = 120
213
216
219
mp
mf
f
223

226
mf
229
f
p
232
mf
f
236
P
Pno
rit
mf
241
Un poco meno mosso ♩ = c102
mp dolce
245
mf
mp
mp
249
252
mf
mp
Q
Tempo primo ♩ = 120
256
Pno
meno mosso
accel

VS

a tempo
R
Pno
S
cresc
(cresc)

295
298
302
rit
T
Vivo
306
Pno
309
312
315
318
più mosso
rit
a tempo
321

II

Andante cantabile ♪ = 88
Pno
rit
A
a tempo
mp espr
mf
p
cresc
mf
1
mp
cresc
f
1
B
mf
f
ff
C
p
mp

52
sfz
sfz
60
D
accel
Pno
1
5
70
E
♪ = 106
mf
76
F
Pno
f
81
mf
3
85
f
Pno
90
G
mf
cresc
f
96
3
mp
1
101
rit
mf
mp
f
1
4

Tempo primo
rit
Pno
mp espr
H Andante cantabile ♪ = 100
mf
mf
p
cresc
1
mf
mp
cresc
f
I
Pno
f
J
ff
mp
1
sfz
sfz
Pno
K
con sord
p

III

29
B
33
mp
39
45
52
58
poco rit
Un poco meno mosso
mf
C
Tempo primo
64
Pno
mp
70
rit
a tempo subito
mf

VS

121
2:3
mp
F
125
129
mf
G
134
rit
1
H
a tempo
mp
139
p
143
cresc
147
(cresc)
f
I
p sub
poco accel
cresc
152
(accel)
(cresc)
f
1
poco rit
a tempo
Pno
156
161

J
165
p
mp
169
mp dolce
mf
173
mp
pp
12
8
K
Un poco più mosso
177
cresc
180
(cresc)
183
(cresc)
6
8
L
Tempo primo
186
f
191
196
f
2:3
201

206
Pno
M
f
210
Pno
214
218
N
224
230
poco rit
235
a tempo
241
poco rit
Un poco meno mosso
mf
246
O
a tempo
Pno
252

257
mf
262
268
(mf)
P
274
279
284
f
2:3
289
mf
1
Q
295
1
mf
301
Pno
305

309
315
320
R
325
331
337
S
343
347
352
358
T

Published by Boosey & Hawkes Music Publishers Ltd
Aldwych House
71–91 Aldwych
London
WC2B 4HN

www.boosey.com

ISMN 979-0-060-13652-8
ISBN 978-1-78454-554-3

This impression 2020

Printed by Halstan:
Halstan UK, 2–10 Plantation Road, Amersham, Bucks, HP6 6HJ. United Kingdom
Halstan DE, Weißliliengasse 4, 55116 Mainz. Germany

Music origination by Raimonds Zelmenis